An **invitation** to the **palace ball**, saying,

"Come to our party, come one and all!"

Invitation

Cinders really wanted to go,
but her unkind sisters just said,

"NO!"

Cinders was crying,
when she heard a CRACK.

She got a shock,
for the room had turned black!

Sniff! Sniff!

Then, before her eyes, unlike any other, appeared a beautiful

FAIRY GODMOTHER!

Taking a pumpkin and some mice too,
the fairy made Cinders' wish come true!

The fairy dressed Cinders in a glittering gown,
and gave her a carriage to drive to town.

The mice were footmen to serve her all night,
and her shoes were glass slippers that fit just right!

"Be home before **midnight!**" the fairy said,
as Cinders drove to the palace ahead.

Ding!
Dong!

Cinders danced with the prince **twenty times!**
Then stopped in shock at the clock's
midnight chimes.

Cinderella ran home, but she lost a shoe.
It was found on the stairs – what could the prince do?

The very next day, he went to the town to find his princess and give her a crown.

The prince saw Cinders all covered in soot,

but still tried to fit the shoe on her foot.